This book belongs to ....

How does it feel when you meet a good friend you have not seen for a long time?

What do you think about trying new food?

See how white and smooth my teeth are!

And my hands are white inside. Who would have thought that?

Hammerfest 5.15am

Did you know that the Sami have a special way of singing, that`s called joik?

boom boom, boom

Aurora Fox, you are free! Please make the Northern Lights shine again.

hat can you do to take care of the environment?

T502 TD

Øksfjord

Skjervøy

Tromsø

Finnsnes

Harstad

Kautokeino